D1432494

The Myths of Newfoundland: Book I

COMING SOON BY ORAL MEWS

The Myths of Newfoundland: Book II

The Myths of Newfoundland: Book III

The Myths of Newfoundland: Book IV

Love Myths of Newfoundland

The Beauty Queen Bandit

The Last Drop

I have a Solution for the Woman with Slugs:
The History of St. John's

The Ballad of Maguson Meade

ORAL MEWS

THE MYTHS OF NEWFOUNDLAND: BOOK I

A COLLECTION

Translated from Newfienese by Oral Mews

Electric Rooster Publishing

Library of Congress Catologing-in-Publication Data Mews, Oral

The Myths of Newfoundland: Book I: a collection

ISBN 978-1-7780735-0-2

CONTENTS

For My Parents, Henry and Mae.

For Sawyer, Colby and Ashton,
three grand kids.

And for Tina,
my love, my muse.

Cover by Donnie Martin.

Thanks Mackey, ya dick.

About The Myths

In the bays of Newfoundland, the myths outnumber the fish by at least a 100 to 1. Whether at the public houses or around a roaring hearth, storytelling evolved through generations as the primary source of news and entertainment.

From the myth of the width of the women of Avondale to the year of the freshwater capelin, it was often hard to distil fact from fiction.

But who would care to do that?

A magician who explains a trick sacrifices the magic.

The magic at work here is how these myths, this generation's old form of storytelling, finds itself in a contemporary place.

You've seen the commercials. You've probably even created the image in your head.

The fog-obscured foreign land. The strange smiling people. The music.

But to truly understand the place, you'll want to hear these tales. The journey is not complete without them.

Often short, always with some lurking moral, myths are myths the world over.

But here, they're something more.

The truth is, Newfoundland is a lie. A beautiful, well-told, entertaining-beyond-words lie.

Tell no one. Read them for yourself.

Jim Mackey

The Myth of the Miner's Regret in Buchans

"The sound of their hearts beating
was the sound of someone knocking
on the gates of Eden."

When Masie Gulliford from Buchans started an online show called 'The Six Week Secret', urging viewers to enjoy life as if they only had six weeks to live, she didn't know it would go viral and empty three of the buckets of blue hope the town was saving for winter.

If she had, Masie would tell her friends, she would never have recorded a single show, as it was simply not worth the hard feelings that festered in the small community over views, shares and subscriptions.

Like most people who lived in the interior of the island, Masie didn't eat much fish, subsisting instead on trout and salmon, along with wild game and store groceries.

This diet caused them to live in a perpetual state of hoping for something better.

That longing had found a popular release online, with most people in Buchans running a video channel, or blog, giving their self-appointed take on self-improvement and self-help.

And because Buchans had once been a thriving mining town, the directions to a better life were time sensitive in a way that only the children and grandchildren of miners understand.

They knew that hope was a nonrenewable resource, which had to be mined over a certain period of time to a certain depth, and no longer.

For them it was little more than silver, gold or coal in that there was only so much before it ran out.

Masie's main competition in the Buchans self-help movement was Doug Peterson, who had a show called, 'The Nine Month Mystery', which urged people to live as if they'd just been conceived.

He also rented canoes to tourist to self-help themselves to the lakes, ponds and rivers that pimpled the forest around the town.

The huge success of 'The Six Week Secret' caused such an influx of hope-hungry tourist, that Doug had to turn many away, which led to some negative comments on his online videos.

He was so busy scrambling to find canoes that he had no time to answer them, which people took as a sign that he didn't care and thousands unsubscribed.

Since its founding and through the course of the mine's life, twenty-three men had lost their lives, two of whom were Doug's Grandfather Caleb and his twin brother Sam who counted Masie among his eleven grandchildren.

Death, strikes, the mine's eventual closure and occasional forest fire ripping through town had drawn the people together as close as capelin, and they moved like starlings when they entered and left the one church in town.

The division between blood relatives caused by self-help videos strained the town's ability to mine even more hope from their fractured psyches, to the point where an Assembly of the Afflicted was called.

This meeting was open to all residents, but only the Afflicted, those who had lost family to the mine, were allowed to speak.

If you don't have the blood of someone who died with a mouth full of earth, than don't come around here with a mouthful of words, was the official explanation of the rule.

Most people didn't think a meeting would make a difference and weren't even sure it was possible to reach an agreement on two life views that were so different.

How would it be possible to reconcile having six weeks left to live with not even being born yet? How could the end of life be contemplated before it even began?

The self-help community in Buchans had never been so abuzz.

Sales of India, the local favourite beer, spiked in the week leading up to the meeting as people, being the descendants of miners, believed in washing their mouth out regularly with alcohol to remove dirt and dust, and to rinse away as well any doubts that might be lingering in their throat.

Masie and Doug sat at opposite ends of the stage in the high school gym jammed with people and questions.

The Afflicted filled the first twelve rows of chairs with the remaining occupied by those who had no connection with the dead and, as was usual, the oldest surviving miner opened the meeting with his underground thoughts on the matter at hand.

Ceicil Holloway, a spry ninety-eight year old, after living much of his life inside the earth where he felt its heartbeat daily, had been diagnosed that past Tuesday with cancer.

He was given six weeks to live.

Having spent most of his life underground, he stated that while the earth is our final resting place, it is also the place of our beginnings.

Then he claimed that when a man and woman laid together and conceived a new person, that the sound of their hearts beating was the sound of someone knocking on the gates of Eden.

And now his own dying lay before him, like a small footpath to that same gate.

His words moved like loose gravel as he spoke and his consonants were sharp rocks.

The villagers listened as a small landslide of logic happened in front of their ears.

The only difference between being born and dying, he argued, was the perspective of others, as we don't know what's happening except we're either coming out of a hole, or going into one.

The people realized then that the two opposite views could be combined into one shared video channel, where people would learn about both the beginnings and endings of days and themselves.

Mazi and Doug embraced and the town emerged from the dark grey tunnel of doubt, holding buckets heavy with hope.

Ceicil later confessed that he'd just wanted the whole thing cleared up before he returned to the underground for good.

He wanted to die, finding solace in the peace he had helped broker, surrounded by thoughts of blue roses that only miners knew grew on their graves.

The Myth of the Vowel Movements of St. Mary's Bay

"The island was littered
with orphaned dialects
from England and Ireland,"

The wind blew so hard along the southern shore highway that it sometimes peeled the white lines off the passing lanes and lashed them into the trees and bushes where they hung like the skeletons of tiny guardian angels.

The paint crews would come out in their bright yellow trucks, untangle the white lines and glue them back onto the highway where'd they'd sit until the wind came up again.

The strongest windstorm on record lasted from October 3rd to 17th in1892 and produced gusts so strong that a minor vowel shift occurred in the mouths of the people who lived there.

A Linguistics professor from the university in town studied the people over a 10 year period and fond that the long O's, normally formed on the back of the tongue were in fact blown forward and started coming out as the short A's that lived towards the front of the tongue.

Being a deeply religious crowd, this caused them no small amount of guilt when it came to talking about the Lord, a frequent subject of conversation in the area.

As time drifted past them, the change became permanent until everyone was quite comfortable once again with the way their words sounded.

Seeing that the island was littered with orphaned dialects from England and Ireland, they figured one more wouldn't really matter and didn't think anyone would ever notice the shift that had occurred.

However, when the outside world heard about the vowel shift through a profanity laced online video showing two elderly fishermen arguing about tides, Phil Freedman, a famous artist in New York City called his agent.

He told his agent that he simply had to go to the area and paint, using the way the locals spoke for inspiration.

His agent was to make this happen, and when he arrived less than a week later, he stayed in Saint Mary's with the Critchs, an elderly couple who lived alone in a salt box by the sea.

Mike Critch was one of the retired fisherman from the video, and his wife Mary was a retired fisherman's wife who always wore an apron at home and cooked with lard, blocks of rendered pig fat she got down at Gus's store.

For the first while, Phil spent his days wandering around town trying to start arguments with the locals in hopes of resurrecting the online argument.

Whatever anyone said he'd reply with the opposite, 'nice day' was met by, 'not really,' but he had no luck as no one recognized him and figured he was just some simple soul who would soon enough be gone and good riddance to him more than a few were heard to mutter.

A week later and five pounds heavier, Phil conceived of the idea that would make him famous all across the island.

He went to work with the tenacity of a fruit fly on painting three large billboards that would adorn the stretches of highway between the small fishing villages that were strung along the southern shore like pearls.

The billboards would be installed along the high-way for the summer and then replaced with copies as the original three were moved to the Museum of Modern Art in New York.

When he finished them though, none of the locals would help put them up, so he hired a bunch of baymen from Trepassy who were more than happy to have the work.

The first one was erected outside Riverhead, which nestled at the head of Saint Mary's Bay.

It showed a block of cooking lard with arms, legs and a face, holding the figure of Jesus over its head, and underneath the image, written in big fat letters were the words, Lard Liftin' Jesus.

The second was put up just outside Saint Mary's.

It depicted the same humanized block of lard jumping over a prone figure of Jesus, with the words, Lard Jumpin' Jesus.

The third instalment had people bouncing off the walls down at the Legion and former close friends have still not spoken since the day it was voted in.

It showed the figure of Jesus carved out of lard with a "for sale" sign hung around his neck and the words; Buy the Lard Jesus.

To this day the rift between those who supported the billboards and those against still runs through the communities like rumours of poor fishing, even though the art installations drew millions of tourist from around the world.

Some things just weren't made to make money off of, those who opposed the billboards on the Southern Shore still think, and aren't afraid to say.

They'll tell you if you're ever down that way, that it's bad enough having the Lard's birthday commercialized the way it is, let alone making money off the way you sound you when talk about him.

The Myth of the Tip of the Iceberg in Twillingate

"A Pinnacle,
the rock stars of the iceberg world
that had one or more spires on them"

Like many CFAs, who were forced onto the island during 9/11, when Marigold Smith from Arizona died ,she was cremated and had her ashes sent to Twillingate.

Mailing human remains was easier than transporting them over international borders and once they arrived, they were stored in the basement of the church in a row of seven blue lockers.

Thomas Dalley, the town's undertaker, went down to the post office every Friday morning to pick up the envelopes and catch up on the latest harbour talk.

His grandfather had started the family undertaking business, and when his father took it over, necessity gave birth to an idea that changed the town forever.

When someone died in the winter, their body was put up on the roof, so they wouldn't decompose over the two to three weeks it took to dig a grave in the frozen, rocky ground.

So, his father decided to open a crematorium and start cremating people like they were doing on the mainland.

It was an immediate success and soon, everyone in town got cremated, no matter when they died, or whether they wanted to or not.

A cottage industry of urns built out of beach rocks, beach glass and drift wood quickly sprang up and just as quickly withered away that July, when Ethel Troke slipped from the shell of this mortal life.

On her death bed she had complained of how cold she always was and no matter how many extra quilts were piled on the bed, or how many extra junks of birch were stogged into the wood stove, Ethel found no warmth.

For that reason, she told her family the week before she cut short this mortal coil, she wanted her ashes scattered on one of the icebergs that lurked just outside the harbour that time of year.

When her teenage grandson reminded her that icebergs were cold, she gave him a look that added two years to his puberty, and reminded him that icebergs go south, a place she'd always wanted to visit but never had.

The townsfolk, knowing that the soul of the ocean was contained inside the icebergs, were fine with her request.

They had grown up with these giants of the north sauntering past their town down iceberg alley each late spring into summer and over time had grown somewhat immune to the magic spells icebergs cast on anyone whose gaze falls upon them.

The town folk figured they were only good for the chunks of ice men would chip off the grounded bergs and mix with their Lambs and coke, where the tiny icebergs let out 3000 year old grunts and pops while they drank.

They also knew that such beauty was always accompanied by danger and many a time the harbour had been drowned in thunder claps, satanic hissing and groaning as one of them rolled and broke like a promise in a young girl's locket.

At first, the ashes of the recently no more, were put in a mason jar and thrown at an iceberg from a fast moving speedboat, until Don Comden from nearby Fogo Island got his pilot's license, bought a plane and half the undertaking business.

He put up a website and ran online advertising campaigns that targeted the CFAs from 9/11, who had developed a unique bond with the place and its people that can only be forged with fire.

A video that showed the icebergs went viral, and soon people from all over the world wanted to ride them south as well and join the slow moving caravan to eternity .

And people liked the idea of their loved one's soul mingling with the soul of the ocean and this gave them a much needed tablespoon of comfort.

The ability to track the iceberg, named after the person, online to see where she or he was, with video updates and other extras available depending which package they bought, was an added bonus.

In June, when the latest crop of icebergs began to appear, lined up like words in a sentence about accidental beauty, Don would fly out and start pricing them and then post pictures online.

Each season, which ran roughly from mid-June to mid-July, the variety and number of icebergs changed, so on their menu on the website, the six different icebergs known to exist all had 'in season' written next to the prices.

Marigold had her heart set on a Pinnacle, the rock stars of the iceberg world that had one or more spires on them

She had considered a Drydock as well, that had been eroded by the ocean to form ponds and passages of water on them, which she quite liked the look of.

These were the only two she wanted and she would not be scattered on a Tabular, Dome, Blocky or Wedge iceberg, as they simply did not appeal to her, although many loved them as a final resting place.

When her children landed in Gander, they took a smaller plane to Fogo Island where Thomas and Don were waiting with Marigold.

After signing waver forms that absolved Don of any magic spells the icebergs might cast on them, this because a man from Wisconsin had lost his speech for seven days after he saw his first and tried to sue, they flew out to find a Pinnacle iceberg named Marigold.

Clutching Marigold and staring down at the one tenth tips of the bergs above water made them happy with the decision she had made.

But after the ashes were scattered and the plane turned for home, they cried as they always did, and as always, Don was glad he couldn't feel the nine tenths of pain that lay beneath the surface of their tears.

The Myth of the King and Queen of Dildo

"Not even the added,
dark strength of their anger
helped his competition,
and Fred and Sandy won easily."

The bartender at the pub in Dildo knew exactly what Fred Thorne meant when he said life was like being adrift on the ocean, alone in a Rodney the colour of Sandy's studded blue collar.

Everyone knew that after his second beer, Fred, a retired English Professor who spent 20 years teaching at the university in town, spoke only in metaphors, except every second Thursday when he drank blended scotch.

Then he would start talking in the radical metaphors of the French Symbolist, so people had to listen even closer to pick up the debris of meaning his words carried along in the small streams he spoke.

Sandy was the dog he'd gotten from an uncle who lived on the Southern Shore, where tourists, who couldn't afford to fly to Ireland, would take early morning drives along the Irish Loop.

There they'd sip the coffees they bought at his uncle's store while moving through a world of 6:45 AM, before the sun rose higher and the hills were overwhelmed with green.

From the time she was a puppy, Fred had trained Sandy on a treadmill he kept in his basement next to the deep freeze that grinned with the weight of the moose meat it held.

When he deemed her ready, he attached the treadmill to the ribs of his Rodney behind the sail, and wired it to a stand up fan through a series of gears his cousin Jake, who was also an ordained minister, had made him in exchange for three braces of rabbits.

Like all the men from that part of the island, Fred had grown up dreaming of racing Rodneys, winning the annual Dildo Race, and being crowned the Dildo King.

But because he had been born with weak arms, after his mother ate too many bake apples while pregnant with him, the best he'd ever finished in any of the races was last.

Finally, he figured, with the help of his Sandy assisted sail, he had a chance of hoisting the giant Dildo trophy which some people thought should never have been shaped like a paddle.

The official complaints, each holding the signatures of eight independent witnesses, from towns up and down the coast became so overwhelming that the annual clean-up-your-neighbours-yard day was postponed in many places.

After deliberating for much of the month of June, the rules committee of the Rodney Race claimed they had no choice but allow Fred to use his Sandy powered fan.

The big race was run on the third windy day in July, after the wind had lost its bravado and the white caps on the bay turned a quieter beige, and would determine who would wear the title of the Dildo King for the following year.

Ralph Warren, the only person on the coast who had seen every episode of the TV show, How it's Made, claimed Sandy only gave Fred a 2.417 horse power advantage, so it was still possible to beat him.

But on the day of the race, not even the added, dark strength of their anger helped his competition and Fred and Sandy won easily.

In the following year Guy Bryant from Green's Harbour won with a Golden Lab named Blue Bonnet.

In the years that followed, people learned that the resourcefulness and ability to create things from nothing, that had allowed them to survive on the Rock, was still alive in them.

They also learned that four properly trained Chihuahuas will beat an out of shape full grown Newfoundland dog any time.

Because less arm strength was required of the rowers, Florence Reid won with six Shih Tzus, all named after units in the Waterford Hospital, in the fifth year and was crowned the Dildo Queen.

Fred would never be the Dildo King again, but displayed his trophy proudly on the mantle above the fake fireplace in his home.

After eight years of dog assisted Rodney races, the competition committee was finally forced to outlaw them when Larry Decker came down from Postville in the Big Land.

He had with him a 32 foot Rodney painted bright yellow, with six treadmills, each with its own sail and fan, powered by a complete racing team of Labrador Huskies.

The wake the brutes produced swamped two other boats, and Gord Clarke from Blaketown lost one of his three French Poodles to what was assumed a watery grave.

Years later, however, she was discovered on one of the small islands that loitered in the bay where she had mated with a coyote, but it would be years before the Dildo Coypoodle was recognized as a registered breed.

Back in the Pub, the bartender offered his condolences to Fred again for the loss of Sandy, just as he done 12 years earlier when Fred's wife Sandra had passed away just as suddenly.

The Myth of a Thousand Shades of Blue in Lumsden

"Love rose up in Wince Goodyear,
as quickly and as strong
as an easterly wind
on the squid jigging grounds."

It was on a cod tongue Tuesday, late June in Lumsden, when Wince Goodyear met the woman who would fill his hands with meaning and show him how to change the weather.

He'd spend the next 42 years with her, the last five and a half visiting daily at the assisted living home they'd put her in after the dark fairies had stolen the last tiny shards of her mind.

Like many people on the island, Wince didn't care about how big the tongues were, as long as the texture wasn't too fleshy or rubbery, and they came with a small hill of scrunchions piled on top of them.

They were big that day, which caused those who preferred them smaller to complain that they might as well be eating the cheeks or the whole head for the size they were.

She was one of the volunteers serving and when he saw her, he asked after her.

She was from town he was told, but like all townie women of her age, she dreamed of marrying a bayman who would give her fresh fish in the summer, fresh meat in the winter and babies all year round.

She had moved to Lumsden and took a teaching position at the local school the same fall Wince had moved to town to take the electrical trade.

As he watched her move over the floor towards him with the light step of a spring lamb, love rose up in Wince Goodyear, as quickly and as strong as an easterly wind on the squid jigging grounds.

When she laid his plate down and commented that when it came to a tongue, size didn't matter to her as long as it was hot with lots of scrunchions, he realized that until they touched her his hands would be homeless and beg in the street like dogs.

Over the next two months when they met and spoke of unimportant things, parts of themselves strained towards each other and no one was surprised when, within six weeks, they were married.

After the wedding, it became apparent that whenever they touched the temperature in the village rose and soon local fisherman got them to kiss on the beach for better weather, as the heat generated when they did would burn off the fog.

November nights, warm enough to stand outside in short sleeves shirts which were rare as hen's teeth before, but quite common since, just meant they were consummating their union yet again.

Apparently, they were always at it and the summer like conditions melted into December and January.

At first the town folk enjoyed the unseasonably high temperatures and the never before known comfort of wearing shorts after 8 PM.

The record breaking heat also gave the local economy a boost, as snow birds from other parts of the island would visit Lumsden rather than go south to find the sun.

People who watched a lot of cable TV warned that the unnaturally warm temperatures would not come without a price, and soon enough people began to notice that fish caught near the community were substantially smaller and many were born without tongues.

The problem was resolved simply by moving the randy couple's house three and a half miles outside the town limits, where they covered each other in their own company like warm, lazy quilts.

The town still enjoyed the tourist trade from the heat they generated and soon tongueless fish became more and more rare and for one fall even fetched a higher price then their more talkative cousins.

The frisky couple raised three children, two boys and a girl, who moved out west for work after they graduated.

They convinced their parents that the only way to see the grand kids regularly was to join them when they retired.

They were only two years removed from doing just that when the dark fairies first came and started stealing the ends of her sentences.

When talking at times, her voice would snap off like a dry twig and tumble into the puddles of doubts that were collecting at her feet.

Then they started swiping her memories and hiding them under pillows and behind furniture, and Wince would watch as she walked around the room trying to blink them back into her mind.

By the time he finally agreed to put her in a home in town where she could be looked after properly, the dark fairies had taken her muscles as well, and she was strapped into a wheelchair that he pushed back and forth the hallway, to the cafeteria, and outside on warm sunny days.

Her eyes, clouded white with cataracts, stared off at things he could never see, but he would kneel beside her chair, stroke the warm nearness of her cheek, and whisper that they were still a thousand shades of blue.

In the final pewter coloured days of her dying, he told her again and again that she was the fire that first burned in his belly.

And each evening as he left her with a kiss, he whispered that he had once tasted the words she kept on her tongue and that because of her love, his hands could never learn to be empty again.

After the funeral at a get together organized by friends, he confessed that he didn't believe she was actually gone until he went to the funeral home the morning after.

There, she was laid out in her wedding dress and when he bent to kiss her, his lips were startled at how cold she had become.

The Myth of the Birth of the Regatta in St. John's

"The courthouse stared down
on the temporary gallows erected beneath it
with cold uncaring windows."

It wasn't until after John Flood, that the crowd in town quit hanging people and started racing row boats instead.

He was the last man hung in public on the island, after robbing a stage coach that ferried money and mail to Portugal Cove, a comma of a community just outside town.

The disagreement about his dying that rose in the streets was not surprising, as he was a highwayman and had always been a scourge to some and inspiration to others, depending on which side of the Kings coins you found yourself on.

The division of opinions deepened the closer his hanging got, until his name could rarely be spoken aloud without a fist fight and bloodied noses ensuing.

For that reason council had, two weeks earlier at the beginning of his trial, enacted a law that forbade the speaking of his name within city limits.

Some people, heavy with opinions forged in the hot furnace of their minds, just couldn't stop them from speaking themselves out loud.

But, growing tired of carrying the fine of a yaffle of dried fish to the courthouse each day, they began instead to invite people into their boats where they held heated arguments about all things John Flood.

And as the ocean belonged only to those it had claimed, they could not be fined the fish or 20 cents they would have been if they were arguing on dry land.

There were no physical altercations.

The men and women would stand inches apart and scream into each other's faces, but not one person laid as much as a finger on another.

Word of this spread quickly to the other communities around the island, and by the end of summer all major disagreements and the ratifying of any votes was done in the small fishing boats that lived in the bays and inlets like dolphins.

In the days leading up to the hanging, towns-people began coming down to the waterfront to watch the arguments.

At first it was just relatives, there to offer moral support and out shout the opposition's relatives, but soon the crowds began to swell and covered the docks.

Carrying babies, blankets and beer, they came down and settled in to drink the late afternoon away, cheering on one side or the other.

The merchants, who lived further up the hill, began to lobby council to stop the gathering, as it interfered with the boats unloading their dry goods and then gorging themselves on salt fish.

Things came to a head when the Sprightly Ende-vour, could not unload the 3000 big sticks of bolo-gna in its hole and exchange them for an equal amount of fresh lobsters.

Her captain, Ross Ryan from Dover in the UK, took it upon himself to fire three rounds from the Endevour's cannons over the heads of the crowds.

He then warned the suddenly silent populace that if they did not move their boats away from the dock and disperse immediately, he and his ship full of bologna would be heading back out through the narrows without unloading.

He was well aware of the people's weakness for what they called baloney and loved to fry until slightly burnt.

Disgruntled, but calmed by thoughts of supper, onlookers began drifting back up the hill while the fishing boats shifted away from the dock.

Four people from Logy Bay were having a heated argument about where John Flood should be buried and agreed to meet the next day to continue it at Quidi Vidi, a small pond on the edge of town.

The following morning they marched in from Logy Bay with their row boats on their backs, and by the time they reached the pond there were several hundred people in tow, carrying babies, blankets and beer.

After a seven hour, profanity laced series of rants that left the air above the pond an opaque blue, there was still no clear winner and no one sitting and lying on the hillside around the pond would leave until there was one.

When those in the boats took a break to catch their breaths and think of curse words they hadn't used yet, a voice rose up from the crowd asking why they didn't just have a race up and down the pond to decide the winner.

A merchant, who had recently been to Venice, Italy and seen the gondoliers' race on the Grand Cana, began shouting out 'regatta, regatta', which the locals called those races.

The crowd joined in, but not being familiar with Italian, they chanted, 'regret it' instead and some of them tried to do the wave, but to no avail.

The two boats made their way up to the head of the pond where a peace officer stood with his side arm raised in the air.

'Regret it, regret it, regret it', the crowd sang out until there merriment filled the early evening air that lay half asleep on the hillside.

Back by the empty waterfront, the courthouse stared down on the temporary gallows erected beneath it with cold uncaring windows, while shadows crept in through the narrows like highwaymen and robbed the colours from the day.

The Myth of the Forgetting Fog of Trout River

"He was worried that if he forgot,
even for a second, that he'd lost Thelma,
would he also forget
she'd ever been with him?"

Like thousands of other CFAs who flock to the rock each spring, Ernie Ford from Tennessee wasn't there to fall in love with icebergs, he'd come to lose his sadness in the cold, forgetful fog.

Each year during capelin weather, fog rolled into the small bays and inlets that dotted the coastline like acne.

While in most places it was little more than a damp, grey nuisance, in Trout River on the west coast, it erased sad memories people brought with them.

This phenomenon occurred because of the nearness of the Long Range Mountains that crept down the Great Northern Peninsula like the spine of a crooked man.

The people who lived there had grown immune to the effects, either because they were used to the fog, or because they drank the juice from tins of Vienna sausages to cure their hangovers.

No one was sure.

Like others on that forgetful pilgrimage, Ernie had recently experienced a personal loss.

His wife Thelma had died in a freak dessert accident when she was electrocuted earlier that winter while making Creme Brulee .

A month later, while searching for widower support groups online, he'd tripped over a website for Forgettaboutit Tours out of Trout River, whose tagline, tell your sadness to fog right off, intrigued him.

But born with a mind as skeptical as a watchmaker's fingers, Ernie checked and rechecked the website and its claims for a twelve days.

There was a seemingly endless supply of videos on the page showing happy, carefree looking people distorted in fog, confessing that they couldn't even remember why they'd come to Trout River.

They'd look slightly confused for a second and then laugh into the camera at their memories, as slippery as fresh trout, before turning and disappearing into the fog that hung in the air like dirty, grey wallpaper all day.

Other videos showed the same people crying on the fog-free hills that surrounded town, talking about the sudden, heavy pain of remembering.

But it was no different than waking up each morning and rediscovering, after a second or two, the loss you'd suffered, they reassured themselves, except the three pain-free fog days made the weight of memory so much easier to bear.

When he was finally convinced, Ernie called the 1800 number under the contact menu.

The first thing he was told by the motherly voice that answered was he had no real understanding of loss or pain, as he wasn't from an island and had not spent enough time near salt water.

Grief, she explained, was an undertow which, during his weekend in the fog, would drag him down and hold him temporarily beneath the surface of remembering.

He would not so much find happiness during his trip, as lose his sadness for a while.

He said he'd think about it, and was promptly told to quit carrying the memory of his wife like it was the runner-up trophy in life.

A sleepless week later he checked the prominently displayed calendar on the site, with days coloured deepening shades of blue, depending on the amount of sorrow to be forgotten.

They were completely booked for that capelin season, except for a recent cancellation on the upcoming weekend.

He reserved it, booked a flight, car, and an Air BnB which the advert stated was close to the ocean where the fog was thickest and at its most forgetful.

That Friday he found himself driving through afternoon mountains, dappled in green, towards the place the voice on the phone had assured him would make whatever he'd come to forget, simply cease to exist.

But none of what he had read or heard eased the apprehension that had gnawed at Ernie with the ferocity of a feral cat since he'd discovered the magical fog website.

He was worried that if he forgot, even for a second, that he'd lost Thelma, would he also forget she'd ever been with him?

All he had left of her were memories, and even though they released small sparrows of sorrow that flitted in his chest, he liked opening the drawers in his mind and looking at them?

One of his favourites was of the time in Paris when she'd drank too much wine on a sidewalk outside a cafe called Amour & More.

She'd told him they'd never be without each other because of how they talked, he spoke in connect-the-dots, and her stories were full of curls like her hair.

Then she'd laughed and the sound of it still echoed down the empty corridors of his being.

He stopped on the hill overlooking the fog that lurked below him and wondered if the only woman he'd ever loved would indeed cease to exist until he drove back at 2:30 on Sunday?

He rolled the windows down three inches as instructed, so the fog could gradually erase his memories, and headed down into the bowl of damp greyness that hid the town from view.

As he descended the million tiny fingers of the fog began teasing the sadness from of his bones and for the first time in months, he smiled.

Ernie glanced at the back of his left hand on the steering wheel, where he'd written the name Thelma and wondered for a second who she was, before he chuckled at his own forgetfulness.

The Myth of the Blue Pills of
Happiness in Baie Verte

"Words base jumped off his tongue and fell to their death on the bar top."

It was early July and the young people in Baie Verte were drinking so much, they had to post blurry pictures of themselves online, or their friends wouldn't recognize them.

The only person under 25 immune to the fever was Maxine Payne, who worked at the Legion where she moved behind the bar like she was acting out poems about water.

Her hair cascaded down her back and broke over her hips as she walked away from Bill Downey, who sat at the corner of the bar, as far away from Maxine as he could get without leaving the place.

Like all men over 30 on the Baie Verte Peninsula, due to zinc levels in the water, Bill suffered from venustraphobia, a rare disorder which left his nerves unable to bear the weight of beauty.

A side effect of the affliction was being scared stiff in the company of single women.

So, small capelin of fear teemed here and there just under his skin at the thought of the unthinkable – actually having a conversation with Maxine longer than a drink order – but he had no choice if he wanted the $25,000.

That was what Viagra, a pill for men who suffered from erectile dysfunction, was offering as the prize for whoever came up with the best advertising campaign.

His idea was to show a woman and man in a hotel room where, just as he starts to take off her sweater, she stops him, goes into her purse, as though looking for a condom, and pulls out a Viagra pill instead.

The camera would then pan out to show a waterfall through the window with the words, Take a Second Honeymoon in Viagra Falls.

Bill knew his idea depended on getting a woman for the ad who was so beautiful that men would have no choice but do what she said and he knew that the woman had to be Maxine Payne.

To build up his nerve, he'd been coming to the legion for 18 straight nights, but even when he was playing pool with friends he still couldn't find the balls he needed.

But, the contest was closing and he could no longer avoid the conversation, so he'd been sitting at the bar for two hours pounding beer and dying in his seat.

When she came back with his beer, words base jumped off his tongue and fell to their death on the bar top.

In a liquid voice that came from a small spring and flowed over her tongue as she spoke, she told him his idea was so lame it needed a crutch.

What men had always wanted, she explained, was both an easy way, as well as hard, and offered to meet him the next day to kick around some ideas.

Within an hour of that meeting, Bill was so captivated by the breadth of her mind that he had forgotten she was beautiful, and the two laughed the afternoon away as they drew stick men and women on napkins in the corner coffee shop.

Three weeks later an image of them being presented with a giant $25,000 check went viral.

Six months after that a billboard appeared on the lip of town showing a couple, blurred in the background, behind a spilled bottle of Viagra pills on a hotel room night table.

Over the image were the words, One pill. One hour before, and underneath, written in an unassuming font, Viagra. How hard can it be?

The Myth of the Watchmakers
Dance in Norris Arm

"He sent a video showing
the delicate dance
of a fisherman's fingers instead."

When a rash of bullying appeared across the skin of Norris Arm, Mildred Williamson didn't go to the town hall to talk about what should be done, she went into her basement and started making watches.

It was an art she had learned from her father when they lived in England, where his time-keeping creations adorned the wrists of people with too much money.

After he retired, they'd moved to the island which he'd visited years before and fallen in love with its desolate, indifferent beauty.

Less than a year after, he died in a fishing accident that also claimed the lives of the two brothers who'd taken him out in their 18 foot open boat to try his hand at cod jigging.

That had been over 20 years ago, but fearing the pull of the ocean and the loneliness of dreams, Mildred had never married.

In her basement she reached into one of the chests that held the watch parts her father had brought with him and could feel time sifting through her fingers as they searched for the small gears and wheels that would dance freely beneath the watch faces.

Those, she stripped the numbers off and painted the red circle and bar of a no smoking sign on them.

Where the lit cigarette would have appeared inside the circle under the bar, she wrote the words, hatred, homophobia, racism, and other like minded evils with tips that glowed.

Then around it all, where the numbers had sat, she placed the 12 letters that made up the sentence, not on my watch, with the n being the 1 and the h the 12.

The background behind each word was a different colour that gave a nod towards inclusive rainbows.

For six days straight, she performed the small labours of a watch maker and, with tools so tiny they appeared to have been imagined but never made, she aligned and connected the tiny gears and levers so that they reflected accurately the way the earth moved around them.

At the end of that time she had made 100 watches and when she advertised them online they sold out in less than an hour.

She called her father's old company in London and after telling them what had happened, they assured her they were delighted at her success and expected nothing less from a child who had inherited the fingers and eyes of the famous Lawrence Williamson.

Unfortunately, they simply had too many orders to fill themselves to take on what seemed at best a popular trend, and wished her well in her endeavor.

She thanked them and assured them she wasn't looking for anyone to do the work, she just wanted them to send one watchmaker to teach the locals how to make them, as she had no spare time to do so.

They were flattered but doubtful anybody could learn such an intricate trade in time to take advantage of the public's quite possibly fleeting infatuation with her product.

She then told them that the island was filled with makers, and the children of makers, who had to make their own houses, boats, sleds, flakes and anything else they were in need of.

It was a bit beyond a quick jaunt down to Harrods, she told them, these people had to make a life for themselves on a desolate island made of rock and bogs.

They then agreed and sent Richard Anthony.

Three days later he stood in front of a group of 20 want-to-be watch makers at the local school and asked them why they wanted to make watches.

One gentleman said he'd love to make some nets instead, as his fingers knew the language of twine but seeing there were no fish left, maybe his fingers should expand into watches as well.

A woman suggested they make a watch with a picture of former premier Joey Smallwood on it and running around it the 12 letters in the sentence burn your boat, which he'd urged everyone to do after confederation.

Three weeks later Richard, who would go on to marry a woman he met wild kayaking in Sleepy Cove, told his bosses back in London that they'd gone through all five of the chests filled with little universes and were in dire need of more parts to fill their growing orders.

At first they refused to believe him, and because he couldn't explain what was happening, he sent a video showing the delicate dance of a fisherman's fingers instead.

Two weeks later a dozen wooden crates arrived and soon the rainbow coloured watches began appearing on celebrities, game show hosts and even local musicians like The Defibrillators and Bucko Johnson were sporting Norris Arm Candy wrist watches.

Mildred transformed her father's house into the company's headquarters with a large watch face out front with the words, Love and Peace, in the middle and running around them the 12 letter statement, It's About Time.

The Myth of Baymonds Fine Dining in Chance Cove

"All dishes were offered in foggy, medium foggy and well foggy, along with totally fogged."

Some people thought fog was just rain that was too sad to fall, while others believed it was the souls of drowned fishermen trying to come home, but no one, except Derek Smith from Chance Cove, thought it could be used in cooking.

He was a red seal chef, the first to use cod eyes as a desert in what became a popular tapioca style offering in most restaurants on the island.

His fascination with fog began when he, along with seven other people from Chance Cove, went temporarily blind one spring.

Because they were from a small fishing village, the blindness didn't change their daily routines, as their feet remembered where they had to go.

For the entire week before his sight returned, Derek would walk down and sit on the end of the wharf.

There he could feel the fogs tiny fingers brushing his face and pull deep into his nostrils the flavoured memories of ice, bog and ocean that hid inside it.

Once his schooling and apprenticeship in town were finished, he returned home and opened a fine dining restaurant called Baymond's and one foggy morning he remembered without meaning to, how fog smelled and how good it must taste.

At first he collected the fog in clear garbage bags, but quickly learned that it went bad after only a day inside and had to throw most of it out.

After that he began trapping it in large tupperware containers that held fresh lamb, moose and seal which he marinaded for 12 hours before cooking.

It was promising, but Derek realized he would have to infuse meat using a hypodermic needle to get the true fogginess he was hungry for.

The following Thursday the fog sat so heavy and contented on the village that people's feet could no longer remember where they were going and carried several into the bay.

The food critic from a New York magazine who'd been boarding with the Upshalls for over a week after he heard through the Grapevine, a bar on

Water Street in town, what Derek was up to finally smiled.

Afterwards, in his review, he waxed that the lamb tasted like it had run through fields of bake apples, brushed against bushes of black berries, kicked up peat moss and swam in the briny ocean on its way to his table.

He finished the lengthly and glowing review by stating that the lamb tasted like it had lived a short, happy and adventurous life.

Soon all fine dining restaurants on the island offered fog infused wild game, fish and locally harvested meat.

Because of the strength of its flavours, all dishes were offered in foggy, medium foggy and well foggy, along with totally fogged for those with an appreciation for expensive scotch.

Foodies worldwide, rushed online and urged people to go to the island and try it, but warned them that such dishes were, of course, only served in season.

The Myth of Make and
Break Mornings in Harbour Deep

"The bay was as flat as an ex-lover's gaze
when the make & break engine
coughed and sputtered into life."

After Levi Ropson from Harbour Deep developed a crick in his neck from looking back at his regrets, council passed a law forbidding sadness inside the community limits.

Anyone experiencing sadness had to walk into the woods that surrounded the community, or face a fine of 25 cents per teardrop.

People soon realized that looking back at mistakes just took time away from moving ahead, so they all enjoyed the new law, except Levi.

Levi didn't like it at all.

He had enjoyed rolling down the alabaster tunnel of his past and gazing at his bad memories until he could taste their sadness anew.

One showed his father and two older brothers, face down in an angry sea.

It was then he'd learned to fear and hate the water, and at 17 he'd fled to the mainland to escape its nearness.

A second depicted steel and asphalt carnage from that night a drunk driver had taken his wife and two children and left him paralyzed.

Levi Ropson wore his sadness like a badge of honour, it was something he had earned and he'd be dammed if that crowd on council was taking it from him.

Nobody disagreed with him, they understood how trapped he was in a town serviced by the coastal ferry with no roads in or out.

And because he couldn't just walk off into the woods like other people who wanted to enjoy a moment of sadness, he was forced to hold his in like pinned gas, or pay for it.

After the amount he owed in tear taxes reached over a thousand dollars, someone finally said what everyone was thinking, Levi would have to get in a boat to get out of town.

So one calm Saturday morning, he was tied into his chair and deposited into a trap skiff.

He'd been given several shots of Screech to temper his nerves and he even laughed a small pitiful laugh as they were lowering him into the boat.

His brakes were applied and ropes were lashed to keep his chair in place.

The bay was as flat as an ex-lover's gaze when the make & break engine coughed and sputtered into life.

Soon the air was tinted with smoke and filled with the putt-putt of a pulse from a long time ago, as it took Levi away.

Two hours later, a grinning Levi Ropson returned and claimed between sobs that he'd thought the sound of the engine was his mother's heart beating in the womb.

And the slow movement of the sleeping ocean, he thought that was the rise and fall of his wife's breasts as she lay sleeping beside him.

The following week, Levi bought his own skiff and made it completely wheelchair accessible.

On warm summer mornings that filled the harbor with hope, he could be seen putt-putting along the shore in it, with a bottle of screech in one hand, grinning from ear to ear as tears rolled down his cheeks.

The Myth of the Four-Legged
Chickens of Corner Brook

"It was a rooster she named Carlos,
after a bass player she'd met in Cuba."

Fat white clouds sauntered across a bullied blue sky over the shed in Corner Brook, where Daphane Abbott was trying to undo an experiment she'd conducted two summers before, that had produced the island's first four-legged rooster.

The daughter of a genetics professor, Daphane had grown up speaking DNA as a second language, and after graduating university, had toured the island with her father, supporting his fight to have codfish genetically engineered so they'd have two tongues.

At the potluck dinner after the presentation in Corner Brook, she met her husband Terry who, everyone in town agreed, was as handsome as a fibreglass speedboat.

The two were wed that fall and five years later, with two children and house in order, Daphane retreated to the shed and her passion for genes.

Within seven weeks she had overseen the hatching of the world's first four-legged fowl.

It was a rooster she named Carlos, after a bass player she'd met in Cuba.

She planned to breed him with regular chickens to produce more four-legged birds that would not only advance science, but double the drumsticks for Sunday dinners.

The morning she brought Carlos his first date, she found he'd escaped and, because of the speeds he reached using his extra legs, no one in town was able to catch him.

Even groups comprised of the fastest runners on the Island, decked out in expensive sneakers and brand name water bottles, were left in his dust despite the $1000 prize for his capture.

People soon realized there was no sense in chasing a four-legged rooster around and young Carlos was left to himself in the quiet dark woods where he grew into his roosterhood.

On still nights, when the moon hung contented in the sky while the bay held its breath, he would serenade the ladies lying half-awake in their chicken coups.

And although Carlos was never caught in the act, evidence of his visits broke out of eggs now and then in the shape of four-legged chickens which quickly escaped as well.

The town council voted to string fishing nets between trees to catch them, but some people at the meeting argued that the real problem would begin only after one was caught and killed.

While it was easy to avoid a normal chicken running around with its head cut off, a four legged one might prove more of a menace than a meal, Dean Baggs the former mayor warned.

The vote was rescinded, and the town folk decided instead to charge big game hunters from the mainland for a licence to come and hunt their elusive chickens.

And when an online video was slowed down to reveal that the multi coloured lighting bolt hitting the town, was actually a four legged chicken running down Main Street, applications flooded in.

1000 licenses were issued, but not a single bird was taken and word of this swept through the big game hunting community like rumours of pregnancy.

As a result 5,000 of the biggest, gamiest big game hunters in the world converged on Corner Brook the following summer.

All day long, the woods were a symphony of gun shots and curse words, until evening drove the hunters home to suppers taken with the shaking of heads and wringing of hands, served on plates sprinkled with muttered disbelief.

Daphane soon realized the hunters wouldn't stop until Carlos was too old to run fast enough, or too tired to care, and that the rest of the flock would soon follow him to the grave and gravy that waited.

That dark realization pulled her from her bed each morning and chased her out into the shed to experiment with berries.

She concentrated on blue berries, which heightened people's connections with other life forms, and juniper berries, which erased the memory of what chicken tasted like.

By splicing the genes and serving them at supper in a blueberry duff, she hoped the hunters would develop a bond with the chickens and forget how good they tasted.

But when she introduced the pudding to the hunters that Wednesday, they ate every last crumb and still spent the evening cleaning guns and loading magazines.

But the following morning when the hunters awoke they wandered into the woods armed only with their cell phones.

Laughter blossomed in the forest.

The hunters, transfixed by beauty and filled with good balogna, shot pictures of the lush lines of colours that blurred the morning air, as fifteen four-legged chickens led by Carlos, rippled by them like thoughts about long ago rainbows.

The Myth of the Well Welded Love of Placentia

"Where her heart lay broken still,
on the beach rocks of an evening."

Unlike most people who leave to find work, Mary Neville from Placentia never came back home, not even for funerals or weddings.

And although she never darkened the doors of the places she left behind, her thoughts always clung to the shoreline where she had last walked with the only man she would ever love.

A small swell, born far out to sea, rattled the beach rocks like change in the pockets of that evening, while he told her such terrible truths.

She had just finished trade school and he would not move to town with her as he had said he would because he wanted a woman who would be a fisherman's wife not a welder.

The remnants of love moved his hands back and forth on her shoulder as he spoke like small boats on an almost sleeping ocean.

Even when she told him she believed her fingers held gifts that no one could see, he would not alter the course of his mind and, because he was a fisherman, she knew he never would.

That knowing struck like a jigger in a fish and there arose in her the stubbornness of daisies.

It would be the last time she ever saw him, as she went blind in a freak welding accident just three months later, and there being no work on the island for a blind welder, she moved to the mainland and left him behind.

She rented a small basement apartment and found work in a local welding shop where she quickly became known for the graceful energy of her welds which caressed the metals they held.

After losing her sight, Mary saw welding as simply time and distance brushing against each other as they passed, and her hands began to move while she worked like she was conducting an orchestra only she could hear.

In her empty apartment she designed and set up miniature tanks, hoses and tiny chipping slag hammers to weld away the empty evenings she spent alone there.

The miniature, pieces she created from metals, heated and bent to her will, were held in space with welds that looked like they had been formed by the tiny fingers of spiders on wet July afternoons.

She sold them online and soon gained a following but when people found out she was also blind she quickly became famous.

A prominent New York art dealer signed her to an uptown gallery and she was soon pictured on the covers of Art magazines worldwide, which adorned the walls of the post office in Placentia.

In an interview on national television she was asked about the creative process in her work and she explained that what she made was just whatever her fingers were remembering at the time.

It could be anything from the gentle, welcoming curve of a lover's smile to the shape of their voice when they spoke your name.

Each piece sold for millions of dollars before it was even completed and within three years, she was one of the most celebrated artists in the world.

Still, no matter where she travelled to accept awards, or for openings of her latest sold out exhibition, her thoughts lay moored to the time when she'd chosen the future at the price of the past.

She would not, and could not, be a fisherman's wife.

That November when she turned 42 she was named the most influential artist on the planet and flown to Sweden to accept the prize.

There, she drank in the applause that washed over her like rain from the forest, but her eyes could not see the adoring crowd.

They saw instead a girl waiting on the shoreline in Placentia where her heart lay broken still, on the beach rocks of an evening.

The Myth of the Lonely Lobsters of Logy Bay

"His neighbour claimed he'd witnessed wild lobsters chasing a squirrel across his front garden."

Because lobsters are born thousands of miles away from their mothers, they crave companionship and will make friends with flat fish or even hang out with beach rocks to try and alleviate the loneliness they're born with.

Eventually most find their own kind and grow into large marauding hordes that spend their days walking together and talking about things they found on the ocean floor and where their parents might be from.

Because of this carefree lifestyle and absence of adult supervision there was within each lobster the innocence of sea weed which was made them so easy to catch.

So when Ted Caddigan from Logy Bay wanted some to spread on the preddy grounds, he just walked down to the low cliffs with his bicycle wheel.

The town's last surviving bachelor he was an x-ray technician he always wore t-shirts that said 'I'm so hot I'm x-ray Ted', which people felt did nothing to help change his relationship status.

On each spoke of the wheel Ted had skewered a Vienna Sausage, the preferred bait of local lobster fishermen, and attached four pieces of rope to its compass points.

It was soon shimmering on the bottom like a discarded halo.

The lobsters picked up the scent and made their way out from under the lonely rocks they called home.

Once three or four had ambled onto the bike wheel Ted pulled it to the surface with the quick, immediate motions of his grandfather's hands.

By suppertime he had enough and headed back home where he laid them out on the mounds of earth that the potatoes, who gave birth through their eyes, slept beneath.

When he finished he went home and slept alone, dreaming of the sweetest, pinkest potatoes he'd ever eaten.

Early the next morning he went to check on his new fertilizer, and discovered that every single lobster was gone.

Small trails along the tops of the beds bled into one as they'd marched in single file and disappeared into the tall grass by the fence he'd put up to keep the neighbour's cow at bay.

He marked it down to a learning experience and figured he'd use pegs and twine to keep the next batch in place, but they disappeared as well and the frayed ends of the twine told him the others had come back and chewed through it to free their crustacean cousins.

He gave up on the idea and thought no more about it until early August when his neighbour claimed he'd witnessed wild lobsters chasing a squirrel across his front garden.

They dug their claws into the ground and then propelled themselves forward with them, while uncoiling their muscular tails and were able to move at an alarming speed.

Something like a squid only different was how he described it, stating that only the nearness of a birch tree had saved that squirrel from being lobster dinner.

At an emergency council meeting Ted confessed the lobsters were his and was told to get rid of them before the thousands of eggs each female carried hatched and the entire island was over run.

He agreed and having already noticed the lobsters had created leads in the long grass much like rabbits did, he decided he'd simply set snares for them and waited until the next full moon to hang above the fields.

At 11:30 that night he was making his way to the tree line when he saw them.

He wondered for a moment why they'd returned to the preddy grounds and spread themselves out as he'd done, then realized it was just their empty shells the moon beams were poking.

Further down over the hill towards the beach he saw the lobsters who had shed them, no longer protected from the gulls and crows, taking their soft, squishy selves back into the ocean.

Because of the threat wild lobsters posed to children and pets, no one was ever allowed to use them again on the preddy grounds, although the town would talk for years of Ted's potatoes.

How they were born that year with little claws and tasted of the sweet, school-aged loneliness of August.

The Myth of the Gesture of La-Te-Da in Stephenville Crossing

"George returned home,
and within a week there was
a noticeable improvement
in their marriage."

Like many married men, George Power from Stephenville Crossing only pretended he was listening to his wife, so three weeks passed before he realized he could no longer hear the sound of her voice.

At first he thought he'd lost his hearing from eating too many freshwater clams, but the sounds of waves arguing with beach rocks and chickadees serenading apples in the trees out front told him he hadn't.

Then he thought maybe prayers were answered and she'd lost her voice, so when she left the room, he got Jim from next door to see if he could hear her.

He could.

Now that it was apparent the problem was with him somehow, George drove to the hospital in Stephenville where he told the doctor what had happened, and asked if there was a pill he could take, or cream he could rub on his ears to restore the audio connection with his wife.

After an examination, the doctor, who wore the thin whiskers of a mink, told George that while losing the ability to hear your wife's voice was common on the island, there were no known cure for it.

He assured him there was nothing to worry about though, as married couples typically have the same five conversations over and over in no particular order.

He advised George to watch the gestures his wife made as she spoke, as they would let him know which one they were having.

If she sat with elbows on the table and all her fingers touching while staring at the ceiling, that was the gesture of long ago and he would know she was talking about the past.

A knowing smile, while tilting his head and rubbing his earlobe, was all that was required of him.

A tightening of the shoulders, stiffening of the neck and slight pursing of the lips was the gesture of la-tee-dah, which meant she was talking about a relative who moved to the mainland and now thought they were better than anyone else.

A small frown accompanied by slight head nodding was all that was needed to show he agreed.

Tapping her fingers on the tabletop, a noise he would hear, while staring towards the fridge was the gesture of what should we have for supper.

A slight shrug of his shoulders while suggesting fish would complete that conversation.

Staring out the window while shaking her head was the gesture of bad weather.

Looking down and shaking his head slowly was all that was required from him.

If she raised her hand and made a motion of throwing salt over her shoulder, that was the gesture of needing something done around the house.

His reply would be to stand up and go find some work to do.

Finally, folding her arms and staring at the kitchen ceiling was the gesture of lost children, which meant she was talking about family who lived out west.

His response would be to stand up and lovingly tap her on the shoulder as he left the room.

George returned home and within a week there was a noticeable improvement in their marriage.

This spurred him on to start holding weekly gesture meetings with other husbands from nearby communities, who were also having trouble hearing their wives talk.

Their symptoms ranged from still being able to catch parts of sentences, to losing the sound for days at a time, to complete loss of ability to hear their wive's voices.

Soon the group numbers had grown to more than 50, and the meetings had to be moved from George's shed to the school gym.

After coaching over a hundred husbands in the art of ignoring their wives, while watching their gestures, those who could still partially hear felt ready to begin wearing ear plugs that looked like hearing aids.

Men from all over the west coast were soon reporting that since they could no longer hear what their wives were saying and answered instead to gestures, all of their marriages had improved significantly.

Husbands of Gestures, as they came to call themselves, tried to keep news of their doings confined to the Port au Port Peninsula, but eventually word leaked out and gesture training was soon being practiced by married men island wide.

And, despite their best efforts, which included wearing blue underwear to aid in silence, existence of the Husbands of the Gestures was eventually made public through a leaked online video.

The grainy film showed a gymnasium floor crowded by a group of middle-aged men in ball caps moving in unison like the straws of a slow sweeping broom.

Once the video became public, the wives admitted that they had known all along what was going on, and had only pretended not to.

This new way of communicating let them pretend to throw salt over their shoulder in any conversation they were having, which got their husbands to do things around the house without having to wait months, or even weeks.

And because their marriages had improved so much, they didn't go back to talking out loud and instead, at kitchen tables all over the island, happily married couples danced in the soft morning silence to the gestures of long ago and la-tee-dah.

The Myth of the People Who Laughed Freely in Rocky Harbour

"So, stuffed with learning
and reeking of philosophy,
Albert returned home."

On an early August morning, beneath a sky still smeared with marmalade, the people of Rocky Harbour began wandering around aimlessly, in the manner of men waiting for their wives in shopping malls.

Seen at first as strange but harmless, it became apparent after the better part of a week that the wandering was also accompanied by rapid memory loss.

So, when Jeff Garland left his house that Thursday morning and wandered into Jack's store, he immediately forgot why he had come there.

He told Jack, who was ambling slowly up and down the hardware aisle, about what had happened and both men laughed, but not for any great length of time as they soon forgot what was so funny, a realization which only made them laugh again.

This continued for most of the morning until Jeff wandered aimlessly back home and told his wife

Brenda that something hilarious had happened with someone, but he couldn't for the life of him remember who or what it was, and they both laughed at his forgetfulness.

This communal forgetting became a source of great levity, and the small out port community swelled with the sound of laughter.

Soon tourists, learning about the phenomena online, descended onto the small harbour to laugh and take selfies of themselves standing among the wandering, happy townsfolk.

When Jeff and Brenda's son, Albert, saw the videos and pictures, he also saw an opportunity to help his family and neighbours profit from the newly sprung tourist trade.

Three years earlier, he had moved into town to study business at the university there and had escaped the strange affliction that gripped the town in its crow like talons.

Since everyone had begun spending their days wandering aimlessly about and laughing at their inability to remember even the simplest thing, no work had gotten done.

Boats lay tied to the wharf like expectant dogs, firewood cut and chopped the year before waited quietly in the woods, and forgotten boots, bags, hats and coats peopled the front lawns and driveways.

And above the surface of the bay there hung like sheers, the forgotten memory of the setting down of teacups, the putting on of gloves and caps, for the work that sat waiting to be done.

So, stuffed with learning and reeking of philosophy, Albert returned home and called an election in which he was the only person who ran, or remembered to vote.

The new mayor immediately imposed a laughing tax of twenty-five cents that had to be paid by anyone who laughed inside the town limits.

Tourists quickly learned to bring bags of quarters with them and deposit one into the slit on top of the waiting 45-gallon drums that littered the town like gulls, each time they burst into the unimagined joy of laughter.

The only exception to this tax law were the people from Rocky Harbour, who were allowed to laugh freely all day.

The Myth of the
Forgetful Beach Rocks of Collinet

"The knowing crept into his lips
and formed a lopsided smile."

As was the custom in Colinet, when Zeke Diddim's wife left him for a Middle Gut turnip farmer, he wrote her name on a beach rock and threw it off the head of the wharf.

Then he went home where he composed sad songs for piano accordion, while he waited for the salty tongue of the tides to lick it off so he could start dating again.

After eight weeks without any noticeable change in his love levels, Zeke returned to the wharf at low, evening tide and using a monocular he had been left in his grandfathers will, peered into the clear still eye of the ocean.

There was no sign among the pile of beach rocks of one with the name Sheila written on it.

There was a fresh Jane, which surprised him because he didn't know Bill and her were having trouble, and half an erased Robert, but other than that the beach rocks were bare of any ink that tied a person's heart to the sea.

He gazed out over the flat, unseeing surface of the bay as the sun flirted with clouds on the horizon and wondered aloud if he would ever love again.

While those thoughts lay like mud on his mind he returned home, ate a late supper of oven baked pork chops covered with cream of mushroom soup and then went out to his shed to write more songs about longing and loss.

On the floor was a roll away cot with a quilt that depicted bunnies in different poses.

He had taken to sleeping on it since his wife had left, fearing that by staying in the house he might disappear forever into the vast and sudden emptiness of their marriage bed.

Opening a beer like it was a conversation about regrets, he sat down and took to drinking and playing.

Slouched over by the weight of his loneliness he cuddled his accordion, while his fingers whispered to the buttons the sadness they'd known.

The next morning he drove down to Corrigans store to get more of the coldest beer on the shore.

While he stood outside in a borrowed James Dean pose debating how much he'd need, handsome new comer Johnny Bishop drove past, towing his lawn tractor behind him.

Then a strange man went by, driving Sheila's car.

The ground didn't disappear beneath Zeke and send him plummeting through darkness into a bottomless pit of confusion, anger and pain like he thought it would.

Instead, there arose in him the hope that Sheila was happy, and he hoped whoever she was with was happy too, and he hoped the whole world was happy and why wouldn't you?

As the sun fell slowly into the ocean and spilled colours across the sky like slowly fading thoughts of yesterday, he came to understand that love was not what he'd thought it was.

He knew for the first time that there was no lost love or found love, no real love or false love, that there was only always love, and that love flowed through the world about chest-high looking for someone or something to reflect itself against.

The things he had thought were important, the big house, the big bank account, the fancy car, what people thought and what people said, he now realized didn't matter at all.

All that mattered was love.

So, maybe he never threw the beach rock off the wharf, or maybe a lobster stole it as a friend and was now nudging it across an endless ocean floor.

The knowing crept into his lips and formed a lopsided smile.

He got a dozen and a half India and scurried back to his shed where he wrote more sad songs, that in a year would be released as his first album entitled, Jigs and Feels, the World Accordion to Zeke.

The Defibrillators from Change Islands played backing tracks on it, and country crooner Bucko Johnson, a come from away out of Tennessee wrote and sang lyrics for two songs which he judged too sad to be left unspoken.

The album would top the bestseller lists at Fred's in town for almost a year, by which time Zeke had met and married a woman from Harbour Deep, his first and only groupie.

The Myth of the
Argumentative Widows of Bonavista

"It lay beyond the reach of words,
and could only be expressed
through the fragrance of memory."

On the third Friday of every month, the widows of Bonavista met at rotating homes to argue about the aromas of memory and debate how yesterday might have smelled.

In between time, they went for long, solitary walks and collected common things like grass and the fat ends of gull feathers.

These they carried home, and with the steady fingers of spiders, cut tiny heart shaped pieces out of them.

Once they had enough they poured them into food processors they'd got at Costco in town, before tuning the engines by following car videos online.

Over time, these hopped up machines became so powerful that all the little hearts were broken into pieces so small, you could no longer see them.

They were ground so fine they disappeared and the air they became carried in it all the scents of the memories they held.

Then, using only their noses to determine volume, they poured the scented nothingess into salt shakers through the bottom with a small funnel.

They'd bring these to the meeting, and sprinkle the aroma on their wrists, sniff it in small quick gasps, and begin arguing about its effectiveness.

One of the widows, Flo Garland, was even more excited than usual about that Friday's get together at Elma's and was quite looking forward to the disagreements that lurked in the furniture there.

She could hear the other widows picking apart her scent now and it had only gotten worse since they'd joined an online wine tasting club.

They'd bemoan the fact that they were getting a lot of high school, the grass smell, but were missing the pungent memories of being six or seven when time was more salty.

Or, they would say the flavor of the later years over powered the musk of the thirties, which ended the experience of remembering without closure and left their nostrils flared.

Flo didn't care, her mixtures had been selected as the featured scent for three months in a row and she was confident her latest, a Bouquet of Goodbyes, would make it four.

It included seven hearts cut from the collar of her late husband's work shirt and two more that carried the stench of sadness that still clung to the bed clothes.

Like all widows, Flo's pain was so personal, it lay beyond the reach of words, and could only be expressed through the fragrance of memory.

So each month after finishing another mixture, her loneliness was slightly eroded and easier to carry.

There was also the financial side of things, as after the meeting the salt shakers were collected from all the widows, photographed and the pictures posted on the online store they'd started.

Here, people could purchase a shaker, starting at $999 plus tax with free shipping in North America.

It stated on the website that they produced scents where the blunted sweet smell of love lost too soon was balanced with a finishing slight whiff of hope, all held together by the frayed chords of memory.

The name of their store was Common Scents, and next to the logo was their tagline, A Widow Goes a Long Way.

The Myth of the Loneliest
Sea Monster in the Humber River

"He would raise himself out
of the water to stare down at his
own reflection and not feel so alone."

When Ashtonia Pyeleenie, the daughter of the famous Russian shoemaker in Steady Brook, bumped into Humby on the dock behind her father's shop, she thought at first one of the rain clouds that stalked the valley had discovered gravity and fallen from the sky.

In the darkness that only sits beside rivers, she ran her hand over Humby's cheek, his skin under her fingers felt shiny and slippery like the edges of old memories.

Just then an eyelid of a cloud opened and the moon, fat with September, gazed down where Humby lay sleeping with his big trout head laying on the dock and his frog body floating in the water.

Ashtonia's breath caught in her throat like a nervous field mouse.

He was as big as a school bus and his eyes, as round and black as frying pans, opened and stared at her.

He blinked the moment into himself and without shifting his gaze, slid backwards off the dock and disappeared into the Humber River.

Beneath the surface, Humby hung suspended, savouring the memory of Astonia's hand on his cheek before he remembered he was the only monster like himself in the world and he began to sink beneath the weight of his solitude.

With a flick of his frog legs he was gone.

Wherever he went Humby carried his loneliness with him like mismatched luggage and on days when the sky ached with blue and turned the river's surface to glass he would raise himself out of the water to stare down at his reflection and not feel so alone.

Other times he would swim up the Humber to Nicholsville that crouched on the banks of Deer Lake where he would lie in the shallow water off shore, smiling as he listened to the people on the beach laughing and singing while the sounds of their togetherness washed over him.

Night after night he returned to the dock behind the famous shoe makers shop and pretended to sleep, and night after night Ashtonia would come down and sit beside his giant head and sing Russian folk songs for him.

After eight nights, Ashtonia told her father about Humby and his surprise was so great that chickens in near by towns laid perfect eggs.

The monster was not a monster at all, he told her, it was a trog that must have been carried by a storm from the Volga River in Russia to the Humber River.

Trogs had appeared after a nuclear leak at a nearby power plant and were a peaceful, family-oriented lot who tended to avoid people, so Humby's loneliness must have been so sharp it led him to seek Ashtonia's company.

Her father knew Humby had to return home, or risk dying of the blues over the long west coast winter.

He went straight to work and built a giant shoe with an enclosed glass top so that she could ride him across the Atlantic.

By the time he was finished, the two unlikely friends had grown so close that Humby let her father to attach the shoe to his back using leather straps.

Ashtonia climbed aboard, took her place in the drivers seat and the two glided down the Humber to the ocean like rumours of a long time ago.

Her father and mother boarded a plane and flew to Russia where they met the exhausted but happy couple on the banks of the Volga, which smelled of potatoes and tough choices.

The giant shoe was removed and Humby's family showed up with 16 cousins he didn't know he had, to welcome him home.

Before he joined them on the swim back up river, Humby raised himself out of the water and stared into Ashtonia's eyes before they kissed each others cheeks and he disappeared, leaving only a ring of growing ripples on the water that fanned out like music on a still winter night.

Some say Ashtonia Pyeleenie stayed in Russia and became Queen of the Volga, while others swear the family moved to Deer Lake, where she shortened her name to Ashton Pye.

The Myth of the Small Engines of Love in Loon Bay

"When the only things
that keep you apart is space
and stories yet to be told."

After his wife of 24 years died, Clem Abbott from Loon Bay could still feel her beneath him sometimes like the earth, holding him with her gentle gravity the way apple trees hold apples, or clouds hold rain.

He had tried to bury her memory in the garden he kept in the foothills of his mind where he grew restless, worried and lonely in small tidy rows, but could not.

So he rushed back to his small engine repair shop and sought comfort in that world where logic and tools could make things right again.

Being in the autumn of his time, he'd lost the fear of being alone that haunted younger people and was comfortable in the slow solitude of his days.

It didn't matter anyway, he knew, because no other woman could ever replicate the sound of her laughter or the smell of her hands.

And even though she had urged him at the end to visit Bonavista and find a widow there who would help him share the weight of his loneliness, he never did.

He swore he would not allow himself to become one of those who lived in hope only to die in disbelief from trying to find love again.

They had no children and knowing that pain grows by the number of people who can feel it, he was glad there was no one to see him in this strange and sudden light that crippled him.

Days passed like kidney stones.

Seventeen months later a strange woman walked into his shop with hands that smelled like lavender wanting to know how small an engine he could work on.

He told he wasn't a watch maker like Mildred Williamson from Norris Arm, but when it came to motors if he had a tool that fit it, he could fix it.

She pulled a long slender box out of her fringed handbag and handed it to him.

It was pink with Souvenir of Dildo written on it next to a map showing where the community was on the island.

The town mascot, Captain Dildo, was on the other side touting the motorized toy with a speech bubble that stated, your passion will never die with the batteries again.

He looked up at her and when their eyes locked, they blinked seconds into the air that was suddenly drier.

Clem had always told his late wife that the reason she loved him was the regular maintenance he did on the small engine of her heart and the butterfly of that thought flitted through the air between them.

He peeled his eyes from hers and they came to rest again on the box.

He wasn't sure if it was proper to work on a stranger's sex toy, but work was work, so he took the job and told her to come back the next day around the same time.

Long after the sun had crept across the floor and walls and climbed out through the window that evening, he still sat and stared at the unopened box.

Finally after midnight and a couple of slugs of Screech, he put on his magnifying face shield, turned on the light above it and got to work.

When she returned to his shop, she was wearing a green skirt that rustled as she walked through the door.

She asked him if it was working now and he said he hadn't tried it, but that the motor was fine.

And she laughed the way some old friends do when time doesn't matter, when the only things that keepsyou apart is space and stories yet to be told.

She was from Ontario, and was touring the province, and was staying at a BnB in town, and had been to Dildo to see the crowning of the King and Queen, and loved the island and all the other stories she would tell him, while she held him like the sky holds rain clouds above apple trees, aching to burst into spring once again.

The Myth of the Rock Skipping Introverts of St. Brendans

"That bounced across the backs of
incoming waves like
thoughts of Tuesdays long ago."

It's impossible to stand on a beach without throwing rocks in the water and if the rocks are flat, round and ready, everyone tries to skip them and the youngsters in St. Brendan's were no different.

They spent half their endless summers doing that, but eventually they all grew out of it except Darrin Walsh, the town's only introvert.

Even as a toddler he had kept his distance from other people, and the town accepted the fact he was like he was, so they left him alone

The only break he took from skipping rocks was the year his parents forced him to go to college in town, where he even attended an introverts anonymous class, but was devastated when no one else showed up.

After that he quit school, returned home and built a tiny house down by the beach so close to the water that he could skip rocks without having to go outside.

He kept at it until he got so good he could make them skip patterns and write words as they danced across the mirror of an early evening sky.

Sometimes he'd skip one and then another and the two would criss-cross each other as they moved.

And even when it was stormy he'd skip rocks out unto the water that bounced across the backs of incoming waves like thoughts of Tuesdays long ago.

After someone took a video of him and posted it online, people came to town in droves, demanding he teach them the art of skipping rocks, but he refused, claiming he could not give them something they already possessed.

Instead, he set up a skipping range on the beach where the rocks would tell their hands the secrets they held.

So, they would come by his house, give his cousin Sherri twenty dollars in exchange for a bucket of skipping rocks, while he hid in his bedroom, and then line up behind one of the poles used as markers for their turn to skip them.

It proved so popular that the beach was soon empty of good rocks and no one could skip the rounder ones, which took a more advanced action from the hip twist, through the arm curl and whip out, into a 33 degree angled wrist flip to accomplish.

So Darrin borrowed his uncles scuba gear and swam out each night and collected the rocks that had been skipped that day and it was there, under the dark, forgiving surface of the bay, where he finally felt at peace for the first time.

In the worlds the light atop his mask continually gave birth to as he swam, he was more beautiful-ly alone than he'd ever been and would confess later in an email that if he wasn't wearing a mask he would not have been able to stop himself from weeping.

Small florescent creatures were his only company, except for the occasional lonely lobsters bounding across the ocean floor beneath him at break neck speed towards Logy Bay.

He collected the skipping rocks in weighted nets tied to a rope that ran back up the beach.

Then he swam aimlessly around like codfish when they're ignoring the jigger until he ran out of air and was forced to return to an early morning surface the rising sun had painted reds and oranges that danced as he swam through them to shore.

Because his grandfathers hands lived at the ends of his arms, Darrin had no trouble pulling nets and by the time the first tourist showed up the buckets had been refilled and he was asleep with a smile that melted into his pillow.

While outside the people whooooed and ahhhhed and cheered each other on and forgot for a while what it was they had come there to forget about.

And now and then Darrin's closed eyes blinked in disbelief at the fact that he'd found happiness, and that it was simply helping other people be happy that made it bloom, even if it was from such a beautiful distance.

The Myth of the Southern Rock of Tilt Cove

"Along with backing vocals
on any songs that needed,
as he called it, the big cat sound."

When the national grocery distributor announced they would award trips to Barbados to store owners who reached sales goals, Don Collins from Tilt Cove knew his time had finally come and headed home to get to work.

A saucy autumn breezed sniffed at his clothes as he moved along the beach in the lonely way that people walk when they're thinking of their failures.

His band The Defibrillators, had been together since high school, playing the clubs, Legions and festivals around the island and over time had become one of the best known and well liked acts around.

They toured relentlessly and had even played as backing band on Zeke Diddum's best selling album, Jigs & Feels, but despite all the success, awards and accolades, they still did not have a band T-shirt and it was no one's fault but Don's.

He had come up with loads of designs over the years which showed the band's name and logo and words like, 'some days are diamonds, some days are things that make diamonds look soft', or 'no now knows I won't watch me when I will' underneath.

After dozens of attempts he still wasn't sold on having any of the T-shirts as the bands go to merchandise, available on the road as well as online in their Shopify store.

So eventually he put his sketches in the drawer the fisherman who built the house had made for his wife to keep conversations they never had in.

But that day after getting home, checking online and finding out what the temperature in Barbados was, he locked himself inside for three days and ate only boiled potatoes and rhubarb relish to stay focused.

It was now or never, for as much as fans loved The Defibrillators, many were getting tired of following a band that didn't have a T-shirt.

Even the CFA, Bucko Johnson had shirts with a tear drop coming out of an open eye, much like the tongue coming out of the open mouth on another famous band's logo.

And some people were getting so frustrated by the lack of t-shirts that they were complaining about it openly in the short lines down at the grocery store.

But unfortunately, the Defibrillators were the only band that played every weekend, so not following them meant sitting at home on Saturday nights instead of looking for your sweet spot on the dance floor.

There'd be no more wearing that outfit that made you want to shake it all night long to the classics the boys were burning through so fine you thought you were listening to the radio.

Don's cousin on his father's side, Danny 'Big Cat' Collins, owned the grocery store those murmurings arose in and played drums for the band, along with backing vocals on any songs that needed, as he called it, the big cat sound.

Being the largest and busiest store in the area, he was guaranteed to win at least 50 trips to Barbados.

He promised to take the band and all remaining trips would be won by fans who could rock out with The Defibrillators at a secret location down south.

Plus they'd be kept from turning painfully red after booze filled hours in the sun by the protection of their new, free official band T-shirts.

Everyone in the store applauded and then hung their heads like sea birds caught in sudden rain in recognition of their rush to judgement.

Danny marched up to his cousin's house like someone pulling a wagon that was overflowing with excuses.

He didn't have room for one more excuse in his wagon, he informed Don, who smiled and pointed to his laptop.

On the screen was a T-shirt with the band's logo and name, and underneath them in yellow words as warm as egg yolks; Putting the Bad in Barbados.

He smiled, pushed a button and another T-shirt appeared with the same design and colours, but with the words; Putting the Bay in Barbados.

The Myth of the Skydiving Berry Pickers of Virgin Arm

"They would crouch among the bushes
and talk while they sent their hands
out in search of things that were blue."

When Darius Willthorp from Houston first came to Virgin Arm, he organized a public meeting and spoke for three hours about how the beauty of the place left him speechless.

After that he went on for another two about his love for the Argyles, the women's competitive berry picking team that had won the league title three years running.

Finally, at the end of his speech, he tore off his long black trench coat to reveal an Argyles jersey and turned to show the number 1 and name WE'RE emblazoned above it on the back, in the bakeapple and gooseberry inspired team colours.

Then he pulled up his pant legs to reveal the Argyle socks he was wearing, the only ones that could stand up to the rigours of a full berry picking season.

He listed off the team's achievements, including the first and still only sub 20 minute gallon of blueberries set five years earlier.

Because of their speed and deft touch, they were, he told them, the most under utilized and shamefully unappreciated natural resource on the island.

After a dramatic pause, he had assured then that was about to change and the berry pickers of Virgin Arm would be put on the global map because their town had been chosen as a new franchise for his global exporting Company, Chutney Houston.

The island was covered in berries, like someone had thrown a juicy quilt of many colours on it to dry and then forgotten about it.

There were even thousands of acres hopeful berries where not one human finger had yet feasted.

That too would change, as he would fly the team into those areas by helicopter where they'd jump out, strapped to the back of an experienced paratrooper.

The crowd, tired of people talking about what they knew and wanted someone who knew what they were talking about, applauded politely and drifted back to their homes and waited to see what would happen.

Within a year, the factory had been built and a call had gone out island wide for blue berries, goose berries, bakeapples, black and red currents, and partridge berries too.

In the interior, the Argyles were flown out of Gander in choppers at dawn and the thump-thump-thump of the rotors sang in the air they plummeted through on the backs of skydivers into the best berry spots they'd ever picked.

There, beneath clouds stretched across the sky as thin as grammar, they would crouch among the bushes and talk while they sent their hands out in search of things that were blue.

At noon a second team was dropped in to cook jiggs dinner for them.

The multi-coloured berry harvest was then mixed with dried kelp from the beaches and infused with fresh fog trucked out from Baymond's Fine Dining Restaurant in Chance Cove.

The bay women, all experts in bottling rabbits, moose, pickles and jams, then went to work filling the small limited edition bottles that sold for over $800 each on the world chutney market.

The goods were then packed into wooden crates and shipped world wide to awaiting fa

The reviews were instant and instantly glowing with celebrity chefs and cable TV cooking shows raving about this new style and taste of chutney.

The food critic for the New York Times went as far as to say the limited edition chutney carried in its bouquet the memory of every kiss they had ever had.

Another stated without shame that after eating it, they felt like a Monday morning raindrop on an all day blueberry branch.

Soon berry buses packed with CFAs showed up to tour the plant and avail of the free samples they could enjoy with dried capelin, fresh bread and tea.

Social media sites world-wide were soon flooded with pictures of their happy selves, standing in front of the huge sign bearing the name and slogan; Chutney Houston, I Will Always Love You.

The Myth of the Worried Potato Peelers of Shearstown

"As he panned the room,
a knowing settled over him
like tilled earth"

When Roy Vokey spoke at the annual Shearstown father and first son banquet, he began with the line he started with every year; good evening laddies and gentlemen.

Normally the event was something he enjoyed almost as much as a feed of lobster, but that year his words felt like sawdust in his mouth and his heart hung heavy with change.

For in three short days he'd know if he still was the spud peeling champion of Shearstown, or if someone else would wear that crown and he'd be just another potato peeling chump in a town full of potato peeler wannabees.

That title had been his for the past four years and everyone assumed it would be again.

Then, earlier that September, rumours began drifting around town that Nellie Seymour had perfected an electric potato peeler that could undress a spud the size of a man's fist in less than four seconds.

The one he'd invented five years earlier was operated by hand and nowhere near that fast.

Like all the Vokey men, Roy was a weekend worrier and normally only fretted from seven to nine on Sunday mornings, but since he'd heard that news, he'd taken to worrying at all hours of the day.

Adding to the lump in the bottom of his throat he couldn't seem to swallow was the fact that several stores across the island had agreed to start selling his potato peelers that winter.

They'd be displayed up by the counter next to the potato chip racks under a banner that read, Peel of a Lifetime.

The only condition was that he won that years' tournament, which was no longer a gimme seeing how Nellie's motorized peeler was set to change everything but the clocks.

All he'd done was take a carrot peeler, which worked because it and the carrot were straight, and curved it to compensate for the rounded back of a potato.

Then he'd toyed with the angles of the blades and adjusted them until the peel was so thin it only had one side.

If a piece dropped on the floor, people had to take their socks off and walk around barefoot to find it by feel.

That thinness was the only hope he had of being declared champion by the panel comprised of three local judges and a celebrity vegetarian from St. John's.

By the time Roy got to his patented joke about how people thought being a dad was easy when nothing could be fadder from the truth, worry had crept into his tongue and caused it to stumble.

He fell silent and as he stared out over the expectant faces, the answer hit him like a snow squall, instead of fighting Nellie he'd offer to partner with her in the stores.

After all, the two different peelers would appeal to the two different types of people and those two types were sitting right there in front of him.

The fathers, who were mostly in their fifties and sixties, had reached that point in life where they had more money than time, so time mattered more.

They'd want a faster peeler to save the moments they had left and would buy Nellie's.

Why, in a year of Sunday dinners, they'd save a couple of hours of peeling time that could be better spent out in the shed drinking beer and telling lies.

Their 30-40 year old sons, who still had more time than money, would be willing to waste those hours to save a few cents, so they'd buy his.

As he panned the room, a knowing settled over him like tilled earth; it didn't really matter what mattered most to them, Sunday dinner would still taste the same.

A smile seeped into his lips as he realized that so would the potato peel, invisible or not, that would be fed to farm animals who lived their whole lives without money or thoughts about time.

The Myth of the High-Waisted Men of Branch

"But, even hungover and homesick,
the fishermen could out-dance
the best of the locals with ease"

The men from Branch were high-waisted and took naturally to line dancing.

Their physiques had evolved over years of traversing bogs, searching for berries their wives turned into sweet jams that slept in their bones while they fished.

And one of their own, Nefarious Power, had spent five years on the professional line dancing circuit on the mainland before the pull of the tides got too strong and he retired.

Drawn by the gentle gravity of his own fate, he'd originally gone looking for work but was soon recruited by one of teams and quickly became an all-star.

When he retired, Nefarious was so sick of dry land that the first thing he did was spend a year circumnavigating the globe in an all electric sailboat named, *The Some Shocking Good*.

After that he built a house with a garage big enough to hold, ski-doos, ATVs and all the other toys a bayman dreams of when he drinks too much Lambs and Coke.

The other men in town envied him for his freedom to drink and go trouting whenever he wanted, while they had to get up early every morning to go searching for crab and shrimp hiding beneath the surface of a deep, dark sea.

But the toys quickly lost their appeal and soon sat unused, like some people's common sense, as his heart still longed for line dancing.

So, on a beige Tuesday morning in June, he marched himself down to the post office and stuck a note on the bulletin board asking if there were any men in town interested in starting a recreational line dancing league.

Within three hours he had enough names to call the school and reserve the gym every Saturday from four to eight.

The talent was immediate, especially a young 19 year old Jobadiah Nash, who could dance any position in the line with ease accompanied by a smile that whispered, I'll see you later if I'm still alive.

When Forthright Johnson, the CEO of the largest line dancing talent agency in Texas saw a shaky online video of the teams competing, it was so moving he called everyone he'd ever done wrong and begged forgiveness.

Then he sent his private jet up to the island and it returned three days later with 14 fishermen who would compete as a two row line dancing team in a semi-pro league out of Houston.

Because of the advantage their high waists gave them in performing both kicks and pirouettes, they soon became the toast of Texas.

Lavished with prize money, adoration and really cool cowboy boots, the men quickly took to drinking and carousing in the local bars until the wee hours, before they staggered back to their hotel and dreamed that they were home.

Young Jobadiah Nash, who cursed the air blue when he found out the drinking age was 21, was the most unhappy, and even the drinks snuck up to his room did little to dull the distance he felt in his heart.

But, even hungover and homesick, the fishermen could out-dance the best of the locals with ease, and soon resentment began to simmer on the surface of the days when they performed.

After they showed up to one competition, reeking of rum and nostalgia, but still won handily, the editors at the Houston Chronicle had had enough.

The very next issue showed a front page picture of the team drinking at Shoeshine Charley's Big Top Lounge, with a headline that screamed, *High-Waisted or High and Wasted?*

Nefarious Power was crushed, as he knew it was his fault the men had wandered so far from the homemade bread and jam they craved in their sleep, so he went to see Forthright Johnson to discuss an exit plan.

Forthright immediately offered to double their wages, as he couldn't imagine letting the team, who moved like their feet fed on the floor, just waltz away, but to no avail.

Nefarious explained that the men were thirsty for the ocean and that that thirst could not be quenched with all the bourbon and beers in Texas.

Then Forthright threatened legal action, but Nefarious would not relent even though he, like everyone, knew how vicious the line dancing gangs in Texas prisons were.

After seven hours of heated arguments and coy maneuvering, Forthright reached into a desk drawer where he kept happy endings and suggested a contract for one show the third Tuesday of each month.

Nefarious, after bouncing it off the others, agreed and the men were soon home again, stuffing themselves on sweet jams and salt breezes.

Once a month Forthright sent his private jet up to the island and the 14 line dancing fishermen would head back to Houston.

There, in front of an always sold out crowd of over 67,000 at the Astrodome, the bright lights of Texas would shine down on those high-waisted men from Branch.

About the Author

Oral Mews has been a soldier, student,
teacher, preacher, logger, labourer,
heavy equipment operator, smooth operator,
courier driver, ad man, good man, bad man
and a regular at certain bars in downtown St. John's,
who now lives on the west coast of Newfoundland
with his childhood sweetheart.

Made in United States
Orlando, FL
09 August 2023

35919980R00108